UNITED NATIONS ECONOMIC COMMISSION FOR EUROPE

TOWARDS A KNOWLEDGE-BASED ECONOMY

UKRAINE

COUNTRY READINESS ASSESSMENT REPORT

Geneva and New York, 2003

ECE/TRADE/311/14

UNITED NATIONS PUBLICATIONS
Sales No. E.03.II.E.46
ISBN 92-1-116863-5

FOREWORD

The last decades of the 20th century have represented a turning point in the global development process. It is knowledge that has become the engine of the social, economic and cultural development in today's world. Knowledge-intensive economic activities are now a factor of production of strategic importance in the leading countries. They have also become the main indicator of the level of development and the readiness of every country for further economic and cultural growth in the 21st century. Taking into consideration all these factors, the United Nations Economic Commission for Europe has launched an initiative of monitoring and analysing the development of the knowledge-based economy in all the European countries in transition.

The major goal of this initiative is to stimulate the exchange of national experiences, to identify best practices and to promote the region-wide and global-wide cooperation of the UNECE member States, which would accelerate the development of a knowledge-based economy in the countries in transition. It envisages the preparation of country assessment reports on a biennium basis by national experts, nominated by Governments, the creation of a High-Level Task Force on the Knowledge-Based Economy, which will consider the reports and provide policy advice and recommendations to the participating countries, and the development of progress measurements and indicators, policy guidelines and tools to assist countries in overcoming obstacles to the development of a knowledge-based economy.

We hope that the country assessment reports, showing a detailed level of the countries' potential and providing information on various approaches and solutions, will help policy-makers to take strategic decisions with regard to the challenges facing them in the development of institutions, information and innovation systems, human resources development and other areas crucial for the development of a knowledge-based economy.

Brigita Schmőgnerová

Executive Secretary
United Nations Economic Commission for Europe

PREFACE

The industrial revolution of the 19th century and the scientific revolution of the 20th century prepared the conditions for the rise of the knowledge-based economy. Economic activities associated with the production and utilization of information and knowledge have become an engine of economic growth in the developed market economies, increasingly transforming all the other dimensions of development and the entire societal *modus vivendi* and *modus operandi* of the humanity.

What do we mean by "the knowledge-based economy"?

It is not just the digital economy, which incorporates the production and use of computers and telecommunication equipment. It is not quite the networked economy, which incorporates the telecommunication and networking growth during the last decades and its impact on human progress.

The knowledge-based economy is a much more complex and broader phenomenon. There are different dimensions and aspects of the knowledge-based economy:

1. The knowledge-based economy has a very powerful technological driving force – a rapid growth of information and telecommunication technologies (ICT). Every three/four years a new generation of ICT appears. Today, the ICT companies are among the largest corporations. The ICT sector is among the fastest growing economic sectors.

2. Telecommunication and networking, stimulated by a rapid growth of ICTs, have penetrated all spheres of human activity, forcing them to work in an absolutely new mode and creating new spheres. The information society has become a reality.

3. Knowledge, based on information and supported by cultural and spiritual values, has become an independent force and the most decisive factor of social, economic, technological and cultural transformation.

4. The knowledge-based economy has allowed a rapid integration of the enormous intellectual resources of economies in transition into the European intellectual pool, stimulating the development of the former countries. Every country can benefit from developing a knowledge-based economy to become a more equal participant in the global development process.

5. The emerging knowledge-based economy has been affecting other areas of societal activity in every country, including institutional and innovation systems, human resources development, etc. and vice versa. The knowledge-based economy has become an engine of progress in every country. If a country is developed, it has a developed knowledge-based economy, if a country is lagging behind, a knowledge-based economy constitutes just a small fraction of its economy.

The report below was prepared by a national expert, nominated by the Government, and represents an overview of the present situation and an assessment of the emerging trends in all the major areas, constituting the foundation of the knowledge-based economy, such as policy and policy instruments, institutional regime, ICT infrastructure, information system, national innovation capacities and capabilities.

The report was published by the Coordinating Unit for Operational Activities under the guidance of Ms. Larissa Kapitsa with assistance of Mr. Andrei Maevski, Ms. Alison Mangin, Ms. Tatiana Apatenko and Mr. Mitja Jarh.

Contents

Introduction

The rapid development of new technologies, especially information and communication technologies (ICT), poses a challenge for all countries:

- The creation of the conditions allowing these technologies, and hence the new knowledge-based economy whose rise has been enabled by them, to evolve
- Capturing economic and social benefits associated with the knowledge-based economy.

At present, creative knowledge has become the most decisive factor of social, economic and technological development. An appropriate institutional mix, stimulating and supporting innovative activities and entrepreneurship, sustainable economic growth and a pool of well-educated human resources are considered to be the key preconditions for the knowledge-based economy to expand.

During the socialist era, Ukraine was one of the most advanced republics of the former USSR characterized by a significant economic potential, one of the best educated labour forces and other features of a modern society. However, after the break-up of the Soviet Union it found itself in a deep crisis, being unable for various reasons to rapidly transform to an effective market economy. As a result, a deep economic contraction of the 1990s brought about a decline of all macro-economic indicators and impoverishment of the vast majority of the population, considerably weakening Ukraine's position in the world and, hence, its chances of moving rapidly towards a knowledge-based economy. Only recently has the process of transition accelerated, allowing one to assume that the work on setting up the proper conditions for knowledge-based economy has begun.

The paper below attempts to highlight objectively the current economic situation and macro-economic trends in the country, as well as to assess its readiness for the knowledge-based economy.

1. Macroeconomic trends

Ukraine, a middle-income country of about 50 million people, has a well-educated and skilled labour force. Almost 68 per cent of the population live in urban areas. In 2000, the industry and services sectors accounted for 37.2 and 46.6 per cent of the GDP respectively. The agricultural sector with a GDP share of more than 16 per cent has a strong growth potential. The country also owns a fairly well developed physical infrastructure.

In the first decade of independence, the government made limited progress in implementation of structural economic reforms. The shift in major macroeconomic trends in Ukraine has been entirely negative. The economic decline experienced by Ukraine was double the magnitude of the fall experienced by the United States during the Great Depression of the 1930s, and extended for a period three times as long. Fortunately, the fall of the economy appears to have stabilized in the late 1990s, and there have been positive signs of recovery since 2000.

1.1. Main economic indicators

From January 2000 on, the Ukrainian Government has been pursuing a strong economic reform programme, focusing on the most critical areas with broad economic and social implications. Robust reform measures and improved governance, helped by a favourable external environment, particularly the rebound of growth in the Russian Federation, resulted in strong GDP growth of 5.8 per cent in 2000, followed by an even stronger growth of 9.1 per cent in 2001. This was mainly on account of the double-digit increase of industrial output and the good performance of agriculture. According to the World Bank, in 2001 Ukraine ranked 143 (and in 8th position among the former republics of the Soviet Union) by per capita GNI (US$ 720) against the average per capita GNI for Europe and Central Asia of US$ 1,960.

Economic growth has now expanded from traditional industrial goods to encompass agriculture, construction, and food processing. As mentioned in the Common Country Assessment Report prepared by the United Nations Country Team in Ukraine in December 2001 (most of the information presented below was taken from this report), a consequence of the prolonged economic decline, however, is that industry is operating at only 45 per cent of its total capacity. In agriculture, however, Ukraine has shifted from being a net importer to a net exporter of agricultural products. Agriculture has been significantly strengthened by the abolishment of the collective farm system.

Although over 80 per cent of all enterprises (producing over 60 per cent of Ukraine's GDP) have been privatized, some have remained under the control of the State. The process of privatizing state-owned enterprises has moved at a much slower pace in Ukraine than in other countries of the region due to a persistent and strong opposition from vested interests.

The steep decline reflected by the official economic statistics during the 1990s was partially balanced by a dramatic proliferation of informal economic activities. Data on the informal sector is sketchy, however. The number of entrepreneurs in the informal sector (i.e.,

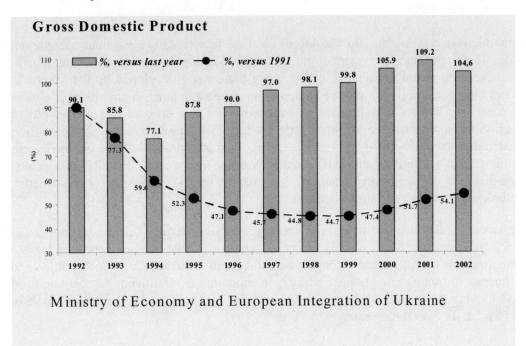

unregistered businesses) is estimated at 1.8 to 3.0 million people. A survey conducted by the State Statistics Committee in September 1999 estimated that nearly 13 per cent of the population aged 15-70 were working in unregistered businesses. Another estimate of informal sector activity suggests that as much as 10 billion UAH could be circulating outside the banking system. The development of the informal sector is a direct response to the slow process of economic reform, high nominal tax rates, burdensome regulations and the need of people to support themselves.

Export and import rates also declined sharply in the 1990s, but showed a significant improvement in 2000. Ukraine is heavily dependent on exports, which account, on average, for approximately 40 per cent of Ukraine's total GDP. Russia, as one of the major trading partners of Ukraine, absorbed 19 per cent of the country's exports and provided 48 per cent of Ukraine's imports in 1999. High global energy prices have stimulated the Russian economy, increasing demand for imports from Ukraine, generating a positive effect on the Ukrainian economy, which to some extent has been cancelled by a rise of prices on natural gas; Ukraine is heavily reliant on imports of natural gas mainly from Russia.

Currently, Ukraine's major exports consist of heavy industry products, including metals, machinery, and chemicals. Whether the country can rely on these exports for future growth is questionable, however, as the technological base of the export-oriented industries is getting increasingly obsolete and their present use of energy is highly inefficient.

Foreign direct investment in Ukraine has remained at relatively low levels for the region throughout the 1990s, representing only 1.6 per cent of GDP in 1999. Foreign investors have been wary of corruption and complex legal and regulatory hurdles. The investment that Ukraine has so far attracted goes primarily to the food industry, internal trade, machinery and metal processing. Leading investors include the Russian Federation, United States, Netherlands, and United Kingdom.

1.2. Unemployment

Economic restructuring and the closing of obsolete factories have put many people out of work. The rate of unemployment at the end of 2000 was 4.3 per cent, according to official statistics, but a recent household survey, using the criteria developed by the International Labour Organization (ILO), put the unemployment rate at a much-higher level of almost 13 per cent. Two factors may provide an explanation of this difference: (1) unemployment benefits are low and give workers little incentive to apply and thereby be officially registered as unemployed, and (2) many workers who are on unpaid leave choose to remain on their firm's employment lists, rather than to lose social benefits and seniority. Regardless, it is anticipated that if the growth of the economy is sustained, the unemployment rate would start to decline.

The labour market demand in Ukraine has changed significantly since independence. One of the pronounced effects of this structural change is that the incidence of long-term unemployment has increased among those individuals, who lack education, skills, and/or confidence in finding employment in the new economic environment. Almost one-third of those looking for work have been unemployed for 1-2 years, and another third have been out of work for over three years

Unemployment in Ukraine: 1995-2001

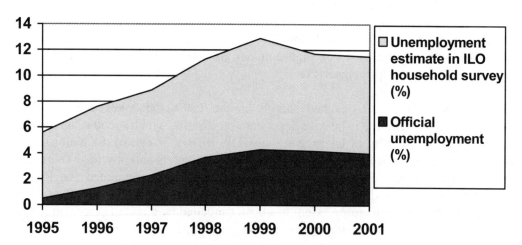

Sources: State Statistics Committee of Ukraine, ILO; Forecast: Quarterly Predictions

1.3. Population income

Despite the recent upturn of several economic indicators, real economic progress has yet to be experienced by the overwhelming majority of Ukrainians. Average real wage is now less than 40 per cent of the 1992 level. Nevertheless, the years of steep decline in real wages appear to be over. Real wages have been creeping upwards since 1999, and the trend is projected to continue. Many of those who are employed, however, receive their wages late and/or are paid in kind. In April 2001, public and private sector wage arrears stood at a total of 4.6 billion UAH, most of which in the private sector. The Government plans to eliminate all public sector wage arrears in the near future.

Change in Real Income

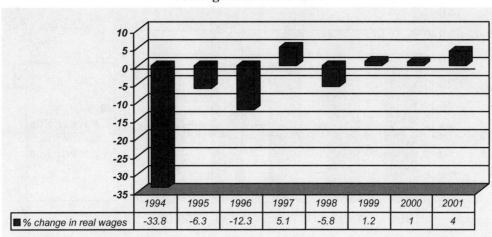

	1994	1995	1996	1997	1998	1999	2000	2001
■ % change in real wages	-33.8	-6.3	-12.3	5.1	-5.8	1.2	1	4

Sources: International Centre for Policy Studies, Quarterly Predictions, Kiev, July 2001

1.4. Inflation

The rate of inflation was high, but seems to have started to fall from 25 per cent in 2000 to 10 per cent in 2002.

Inflation - Consumer Price Index (% change over previous year)

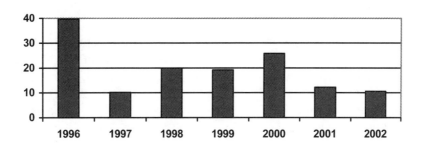

Sources: State Statistics Committee of Ukraine for 1996-2000; Forecasts for 2001-2002: "Brief Analysis of the Draft State Budget for 2002", Verkhovna Rada, Fiscal Analysis Office, 19 September, 2001

1.5. Poverty

Although national statistics showed a significant decline in the number of people in poverty from 1999 to 2000, the percentage of people living below the poverty line remains high. During the prolonged economic depression, a large segment of the population has felt that their welfare has deteriorated. More adaptable members of society have moved into the rapidly expanding informal sector and begun to participate in the market economy. Many others, however, lack opportunities or capacity to find work or to become self-employed. Among these people are many vulnerable groups, pensioners, youth, the disabled, ethnic minorities and single mothers, who require urgent attention.

Poverty in Ukraine

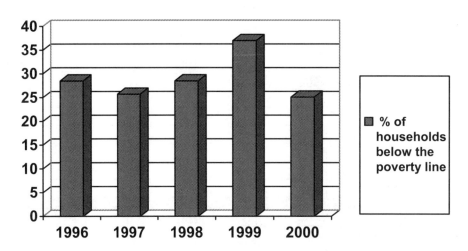

Source: State Statistics Committee of Ukraine. Note: The method of calculating the percentage of the population living in poverty was substantially revised in 1999. Results for 1996-98 are not strictly comparable with 1999-2000.

As can be seen from the above graph, 25.1 per cent of the population was categorized as living in poverty in 2000 (the poverty line of 118.3 UAH per month). However, according to the most recent survey of 8,000 households carried out by the State Statistics Committee in 2000, over 80 per cent of Ukrainians described themselves as poor, saw no chance of escaping poverty in the short term, and expected to be poor in old age. Only 3 per cent of households in the survey had a per capita income of over 300 UAH per month (US$ 56), the suggested minimum required for food, shelter, and medical care.

According to World Bank data, in 1999, 2.9 per cent of the population lived on less than US$ 1 a day and 31 per cent of the population lived on less than US$ 2 a day. In terms of the Gini coefficient, income inequality was 29 per cent in 1999, with the share of 20 per cent of the poorest population at 8.8per cent and the share of 20 per cent of the richest population at almost 38 per cent. Therefore, poverty and inequality have become a major factor impeding the development of the knowledge-based economy in Ukraine.

In general, it may be acknowledged that during the last few years there has been an overall improvement of economic performance of Ukraine due to considerable efforts of the Ukrainian Government to accelerate democratic, institutional and fiscal reforms, and large-scale privatization, and to improve the legislative base. At the same time, it should be noted that the legacy of almost ten years of economic stagnation, corruption, poverty and informalization of economic activities might prolong the passage to a knowledge-based economy as compared with other transition economies.

2. Innovation policy

An effective innovation policy is seen as a major prerequisite for developing a knowledge-based economy in any country. A characteristic feature of the current innovation policy in Ukraine is the well-stated intention to exploit scientific technological innovations for the purpose of economic growth. In reality, however, this policy has not been implemented. Many economists and politicians in Ukraine believe that an active innovative policy requires large resources, which could become available only when economic stability is achieved. As a result, the problems of innovative development remain off the current economic policy agenda of Ukraine. At the same time, there is a direct connection between the absence of innovative reconstruction and the menace of further economic decline of Ukraine.

2.1. Financing R&D

Lack of appropriate financing of scientific and technological spheres of the Ukrainian economy, in particular from the public budget, is a major reason for their slow

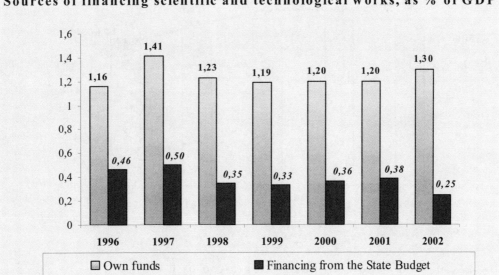

Sources of financing scientific and technological works, as % of GDP

Ministry of Economy and European Integration of Ukraine

development. According to the World Bank, the expenditure on R&D continues to fall: in the late 1980s the GDP share of the R&D expenditure accounted for approximately 3 per cent, in 1995, 1.2 per cent of GNI was spent on these activities, while in 2001 only 1.0 per cent of GNI was channelled to this sector.

The share of the Government resources in R&D financing remains at a very low level, and the major source of R&D financing has in fact been the own resources of the entities

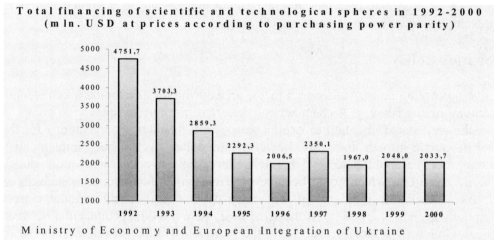

Total financing of scientific and technological spheres in 1992-2000 (mln. USD at prices according to purchasing power parity)

Ministry of Economy and European Integration of Ukraine

involved in these activities. Regrettably, the number of industrial enterprises that apply innovations in their activities continues to fall in absolute and relative terms: from 1700 (18.7 per cent of total) in 1998 to 1506 (14.6 per cent of total) in 2002.

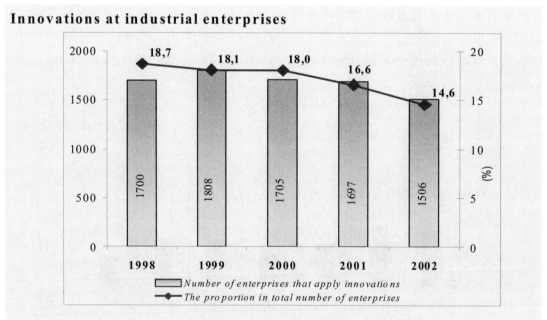

Innovations at industrial enterprises

Ministry of Economy and European Integration of Ukraine

Technological changes, especially in the area of fundamental and infrastructural scientific-technical innovations, are inseparably linked to the production of new science-intensive capital goods that demand considerable goal-driven investment. Given the low level of investment in innovation, the country could lose future opportunities for dynamic development, even if it accomplishes significant achievements in the R&D sphere.

However, in Ukraine, an effective mechanism for attracting investment resources in the R&D area has not been created. The present state of the R&D programmes does not guarantee positive results. Ministries are overburdened with the necessity of collaborating with traditional form of production and are not sufficiently motivated towards restructuring and modernizing their respective branches of production. Private commercial structures, in their turn, cannot carry out long-term projects that would secure fundamental technological

Dynamics of individuals in doctoral and post-doctoral education

Ministry of Economy and European Integration of Ukraine

change. Foreign investments are mainly directed towards traditional production that may have an export potential in the short run.

2.2. Human resources

The lack of sufficient R&D financing leads to the level of remuneration of researchers engaged in R&D, which is much lower than that in the advanced market economies. This is one of the reasons why many scientists and researchers have been leaving this sphere for other sectors of the national economy, including the informal sector, or moving abroad. According to the latest UNDP Human Development Report, the number of scientists and engineers engaged in R&D was 2.121 per million inhabitants in 2001 while in 1995 the corresponding figure was 3.169 (within the range of the 15 most developed countries). But still, the existence of a pool of well-educated and highly skilled people continues to be an important asset of Ukraine that could ensure a rapid sustainable recovery if the appropriate conditions were set up for their proper utilization. The latest data show that since 2000 the number of persons possessing scientific degrees has been on the rise.

Another positive trend is an increase in the total number of students in higher education.

In general, it should be acknowledged that the Ukrainian Government has been trying, since recently, to pursue an innovation policy aimed at modernizing the national economy but the lack of financial resources hampers its efforts. Nonetheless, the economic recovery underway has created opportunities for a successful implementation of this policy.

3. Prospects of creating a knowledge-based economy

3.1. National strategy

The national strategy of Ukraine with regard to the knowledge-based economy is, to some extent, revealed in the Government White Paper on Information Communication Technologies and Internet which provides a framework for developing a new version of the National Programme on Informatization.

This analytical document defines the goals of the Internet development in Ukraine as follows:

- Development of a national component of the global Internet and the reinforcement of Ukraine's role in the global information society;
- Creation of conditions for provision of broadband Internet access and other both domestic and international information resources;
- Effective application of the Internet as a powerful resource for further development of national education, research, culture and entrepreneurship;
- Promotion of international partnerships; and
- Provision of information on current societal developments in Ukraine by means of ICT.

The main purposes of the Internet development in Ukraine are outlined as follows:

- Build up of sufficient economic, legal and technical conditions for the provision of broadband Internet access to citizens, educational establishments, scientific and other organizations of any property form, state and local authorities and entrepreneurs;
- Expansion and advancement of objective political, economic, legal, ecological, scientific, cultural and other relevant e-contents that are elaborated by the State and local authorities, educational establishments, scientific and cultural organizations, archives, libraries, museums etc, concerning Ukraine's development;
- Improvement of legislation and regulatory framework to enable the key players in the ICT market, dealing with production, implementation, distribution and storage of electronic information, to operate effectively and efficiently. This also includes: further improvement of the protection of intellectual property rights;
- Enhancement of access to both national and international information resources;
- Ensuring citizens' constitutional rights to free accumulation, storage, use and distribution of information, and freedom of speech and expression;
- Development and introduction of modern computerized technologies in the system of the public administration, financial sphere, entrepreneurial activity, education and, finally, provision of legal aid;
- Guaranteeing State support of infrastructure development aimed at the provision of on-line services;
- Provision of affordable access to broadband Internet and other relevant information resources and services to educational establishments, scientific organizations, NGOs, as well as to museums, libraries, other cultural and medical establishments, including those situated in rural areas;

- Guaranteeing security of information and protection of consumers

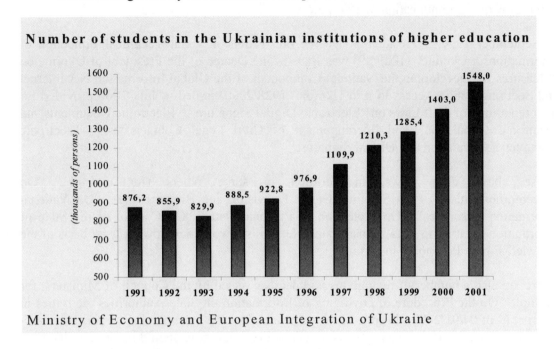

Number of students in the Ukrainian institutions of higher education

Ministry of Economy and European Integration of Ukraine

- Formation and further advancement of information resources.

It is expected that the concept of ICT and Internet development strategy will be realized in three stages:

The first stage (two years) foresees the implementation of measures aimed at modernization of the information system including its convergence

The second stage (two years) envisages the establishment of a national integrated information infrastructure which will include: information resources (both state-owned and private), search mechanisms (portals, catalogues, etc.), legal and economic infrastructure, which will secure the development of the information environment, state system of information security, system of training of specialists and, therefore, a national integrated information system.

The third stage (one year) anticipates the elaboration and further realization of political, economic and financial preconditions in order to fasten the inclusion of the national integrated information system into the global information marketplace.

The above strategy is a clear demonstration of the commitment of Ukraine to develop ICT and Internet capacity as a major tool of advancement of the road towards knowledge-based economy.

3.2. Legislative basis

"E-government" is not a mechanical union of ICT and government. This is a new philosophy of the Governance based on a solid legislative basis. Such a basis has started to be developed in Ukraine at the end of the 1990s, although a number of laws pertaining to this sphere already existed (Law on Information of 1992, Law on Information Security of 1994, Law on Communication of 1995, etc.).

In September 1999, a Presidential Decree on "Provision about Technical Protection of Information in Ukraine" (1229/99) was issued. The Decree of the President of Ukraine on "Measures for Developing the National Component of the Global Information Net Internet and Securing Public Access to it in Ukraine" (928/2000) issued in July 2000 provided for the preparation of draft Laws on "Electronic Digital Signature", "Electronic Documents and Electronic Circulation" and "Arrangement of Civil Legal Contacts using Electronic Documents Circulation and Digital Signature".

These above draft Laws, in addition to some others (for example: "On Telecommunications", "On Satellite, Cable Television and Broadcasting", "On National Information Resources", "On protection of Personal Data", "On Control of the State of Information Security in Data Transmission Networks") would lay down a legal basis of the knowledge-based economy in Ukraine.

There are also a number of regulations and decrees issued by the Council of Ministers, for example "On the Procedure of Divulging of Information on State Authorities' activities in Internet (3 of 04/01/2002). In spite of the presence of such a huge number of normative acts and laws related to ICTs, many analysts believe that a lot more should be done to increase their efficiency and effectiveness and to make them compatible with international legislature. At present, the above draft laws are being widely discussed and it is hoped they will be adopted soon.

Another initiative expected to have a profound impact on the ICT sphere in the country is the "Electronic Ukraine" Programme, which is still in the process of formulation. It aims at developing a basis for dynamic knowledge-based economy with a common information environment, modern technologies of telecommunication and computerization.

3.3. "Electronic Ukraine" programme

The "Electronic Ukraine" Programme is based on the fundamental rules of the EU "Electronic Europe Plus" Programme, as the overall objective and tools for its implementation are identical to those which will be used by the countries-candidates for EU accession in the implementation of the "Electronic Europe Plus" Programme. The Programme will be carried out in cooperation with the EU member countries and countries-candidates for accession.

The main purpose of the "Electronic Ukraine" Programme is to promote the creation of a modem e-market economy in Ukraine and to ensure its competitiveness. It takes into account the real situation of society, its readiness and available opportunities for introducing the newest information and communication technologies. The criteria of the "Electronic Europe Plus" Programme are applied for evaluating the current state of the "Electronic Ukraine" Programme's implementation.

Main tasks

The creation and implementation of the "Electronic Ukraine" programme means carrying out the following main tasks that are important for the development of ICT in Ukraine:

creation of a basis of the information society; cheaper, faster and more reliable Internet for all; development of human potential; and promotion of the use of modern information technologies. Successful implementation of these tasks will result in the introduction of new mechanisms in the relationship between the people and authority, between the people, enterprises and social organizations.

Task 1. Creation of a basis of the information society

(a) Development of a modern telecommunication infrastructure accessible to all people

The European choice of Ukraine means that it must put into effect a gradual liberalization of the telecommunications sector and adhere to market principles for its development. At the same time, the creation of socially favourable conditions for delivering ICT services as a universal service for all Ukrainian citizens is necessary. For this it is necessary to complete the privatisation process in the field of telecommunications, to determine the basis for creating regulatory bodies in this area in accordance with the requirements of European legislation, and to introduce effective regulatory policies.

The purpose of this task is also to increase the number of potential Internet network users up to 10 million in the near future (in the following 3 years). Thus, a significant part of the adult population of the country would have an opportunity to use the advantages of all modem products and ICT services and would be more actively involved in the process of management through the services of e-government.

(b) Creation of a national information resources system

Creation of a national information resources system will ensure:

- Strengthening of the independence of State information;
- Development of a manufacturing infrastructure and providing the population with information products and services;
- Growth of the information culture of the population;
- Distribution of information about the development of Ukrainian information space on the Internet;
- Increase of the efficient functioning of all branches of authority using the accumulated information resources; and
- More dynamic organization of information interaction during the settling of complex problems.

At the same time, it is necessary to make certain that the content of Ukrainian information resources are understandable by a European consumer, therefore translation into the basic European languages should be available in all national web-resources.

(c) Creation of a nation-wide system in order to acquaint the population with the basics of ICT products and means

A network of common computer centres is necessary to carry out of the following tasks:

- Free-of-charge training of all those in Ukraine who wish to learn the basics of work with ICT and the Internet network;
- Opportunity to use the Internet network with socially acceptable prices for all those in Ukraine who wish to do so; and
- Supply the services that should be created within the framework of the Programme for all those in Ukraine who want them.

(d)   Creation of normative and lawful bases for the information society functioning

(e)   Creation of an integrated information-analytical system for the authorities and institutions of local governance

The goal of the integrated information-analytical system of the Ukrainian authorities and institutions of local governance is an integration of their existing information systems into a uniform information-analytical complex. The purposes of this complex are the following:

- Improvement of state management;
- Efficiency, reliability, availability and confidentiality of the information within the authorities and institutions of local governance;
- Increasing the efficiency and achieving a qualitatively new level in the decision-making process; and
- Operative interaction of the central authorities with the institutions of the local governance.

This would lead to an increase of economic growth, population welfare, and the level of social protection. It could be considered as a step towards the democratisation of the activities of the authorities with regard to access to and use of state sector information, and to the citizens' interaction with all branches of the state authorities.

Task 2. Cheaper, faster and more reliable Internet for all

(a)   Access to the Internet as a universal service

(b)   Supplying scientists and students with fast Internet

High-speed communication networks will ensure new conditions for international scientific and technical cooperation and information interchange. They will help to attract Ukrainian scientists to the projects that are carried out in any country of the world. The access to the most powerful foreign supercomputer resources would enable Ukrainian scientists to implement biological, meteorological, physical, and other research experiments.

(c)   Creation of protected networks and application of intellectual cards

The main task is to build the trust of Internet users in the reliability and safety of data exchange by preventing data losses, distortion and non-authorized access to their data. The level of security should be high enough to minimize the harm that can be inflicted upon the participants in electronic commerce transactions.

Task 3. Development of a human potential

(a) Complete computer literacy for young people

The meaning of this task is to ensure that all university students – and in the near future all high school graduates – will have ICT skills. It will help to increase labour productivity potential through improvement of professional skills in all fields of the economy, the attractiveness of the Ukrainian economy for foreign investors and to provide Ukrainian consumers with world-quality national production. This task can be carried out in close cooperation with the programmes targeting the computerization of educational institutions.

(b) Creation of conditions for the intellectual economy

(c) Access for all to the opportunities of the information society

People with disabilities would have new work opportunities through the development of the information society in Ukraine. They could work in data processing, computer design, software development and other information processing work without leaving their homes.

(d) Development of a national software industry

Giving the Ukrainian human resources and the existance of top-class mathematical schools, a growing exposure of Ukrainian students and scientists to the world informational resources and other cultures, and an associated better understanding of demand for sofware in the global markets, will contribute to a right mix of capacities, capabilities and incentives needed for the development of a national software industry.

Task 4. Distribution of modern information technologies

(a) Creation of an e-government system - from informing up to delivering of services

The system of electronic government provides the Ukrainian people with operative and unbiased information concerning the activities of all levels of authority – from the central branch up to the local ones. The development of this system should be consecutive and steady to ensure that the system's standards gradually approach the standards of other countries-forerunners in the field of ICT.

(b) Acceleration of e-commerce development

According to the European Council, the development of telecommunications promotes the economic development of the least advanced regions in any country. Electronic commerce is viewed as a tool for achieving these results by increasing the efficiency of the national economy and promoting its integration into the world economic system.

(c) Creation of an e-health system

The modem electronic system of public health services or telemedicine can help to increase the level of the provision of services to all Ukrainian people by means of ICT installed in the best domestic and foreign medical consultation centres, as well as the effectiveness of the work of medical staff.

(d) Development of intellectual systems

In order to develop an information society in Ukraine it is necessary to coordinate relevant activities at all levels and in all branches of authority – from the central up to local government institutions, to integrate efforts towards strategic directions defined in this Programme as the main ones. This programme combines into one: the National Information Programme, Complex Communication Field Development Programme, Village Schools Computerization Programme, and other programmes and initiatives that are directed at technological development.

The programme will be implemented to provide integration of all the information programmes and projects of the country in all the branches of authority, private sector, education and science.

3.4. Fixed-line and mobile communication services market

At the beginning of 2002, the teledensity in Ukraine was 21.2 fixed-lines per 100 people. Currently more than 10.6 million people are clients of fixed-line operators. In general, the existing fixed-line network is outdated. Only 14 per cent of the exchanges are digital and another 10 per cent are quasi-electronic and semi-electronic. Ukrtelecom, the state-owned giant, retains 80 per cent of the domestic market by number of subscribers. There are also private, mostly regional, providers, such as: Golden Telecom, Optima, Farlep and Crymtel, whose total market share does not exceed 20 per cent. Recently, a national fibre optics network, connected to the international fibre optics systems, such as ITUR, TEL, TAE and BSFOCS, has been installed. Currently, this network is expanding, and the Ukrainian users were provided with international phone connections to more than 200 countries.

Ukraine's mobile telecommunication services market displayed spectacular growth rates of 170-190 per cent by the number of users in 1999-2001. In 2002, the growth slowed down to 70-80 per cent. Two operators, UMC and KyivStar, which jointly account for up to 97 per cent of all subscribers, dominate the market. The remaining 3 per cent are distributed among three other operators. At the end of 2001, Ukraine's mobile penetration still was mere 4.5 users per 100 inhabitants, while the average rate for Central and Eastern Europe was about 20 users per 100 inhabitants.

Overall, the Ukrainian mobile telecommunication services market has several peculiarities: all five mobile operators use Ukrtelecom's network to access long-distance, international and local networks; all of them have at least one foreign shareholder; equipment is typically provided by foreign manufactures; approximately 70 per cent of all mobile phone used are illegally sold.

3.5. Internet market

At the end of 2001, there were around 1.5 million Internet users in total (penetration rate is 3 per cent), 600,000 were active users. In this area, Ukraine lags far behind Central and East European countries (Estonia – 26.3 per cent, Lithuania – 17.2 per cent, Poland – 13 per cent at the end of 2000). The number of active users is growing at the rate of 40 per cent and is expected to rise to 900,000 by the end of 2002. Kiev is the leader by this criterion (55 per cent of all Ukrainian users), followed by large regional cities (Odessa, Dnepropetrovsk, Donetsk, Kharkov, Lvov, Zaporozhie) – 29 per cent.

Prior to December 1997, provision of the Internet services was subject to licensing. At that time, there were 103 ISPs in Ukraine. The abolition of mandatory licensing has stimulated the growth of the number of ISPs. In 2001, there were 238 ISPs in Ukraine, around 70 of them are operating in Kiev. The vast majority of the Internet users use dial-up access and only 10 per cent of the corporate users use leased lines. The ISP market is on the edge of consolidation – there are around 30 first and second level ISP that occupy up to 80 per cent of the market. It is expected that only up to 10 first level ISPs and up to 15 second level ISPs will survive in the long run.

Differing from the United States and Western Europe, the Ukrainian market for Internet services depends more on the availability of telecom infrastructure and PCs than on the demand for ISP services. Considering that the sale of desktop PCs manufactured in Ukraine equalled approximately 200,000 units in 2001, and the projected market annual growth for the next years is expected to beat 25 per cent, the Ukrainian market for Internet services is likely to continue to grow at the rate of 40 per cent in the mid-term.

3.6. E-commerce

While e-commerce was almost non-existent in 1999, by the end of 2000 the number of on-line stores approached 40. In February 2002, the Ukrainian e-commerce directory numbered 182 online stores. Ukrainian e-stores, in most cases, make their own delivery. Cash on delivery is the most popular payment method. Advance payment is the second most popular method – it is offered by 80 per cent of the e-stores surveyed. In July 2001, one e-store began to accept credit card payment. It should be mentioned that, in October 2001, only about 1.5 million Ukrainians had credit/debit cards (3 per cent of the population).

According to one research survey, in February 2001, only 6 per cent of all Ukrainian Internet users had made on-line purchases. Another 7 per cent were "off-line shoppers", which means that they bought off-line, as a result of their on-line information search. Additional 7 per cent stated that they were planning to buy on-line within the next 6 months, which implies that, by the end of 2001, the number of on-line shoppers doubled.

In general, it should be acknowledged that despite its current low level of development, B2B will start growing in the near future. There are a handful of portals that provide marketplaces for businesses. However, the amount of their trade is negligible and their facilities are inadequate. At the same time, with the development of Internet infrastructure and growth of computerization of businesses, the need for B2B services will grow substantially. B2C seem ready to grow significantly in the coming years. Web-advertising currently occupies a small share of total advertising and has much room for growth.

E-commerce has been developing slowly due to several factors, the main one being poor infrastructure (including the underdeveloped banking sector and low Internet penetration), lack of legislation and low living standards of the population. The annual turnover of the retail e-commerce was estimated at US$ 1 million in 2001. It is expected, however, that the consumer e-commerce segment will generate over US$ 65 million in revenue in 2005, taking over 0.4 per cent of the country's retail sales.

3.7. Future directions

The cornerstone of wide application of ICTs is the further liberalization of the Ukrainian market. The State will without doubt continue to play a significant role in the process of building up an information society. Low social motivation has a restricting impact on the development of Internet in Ukraine. Although Ukraine belongs to the world developed countries in terms of human resources development, the majority of scientists, scholars and the rest of the educated population simply do not derive any significant benefits from the application of ICTs and Internet, particularly in their daily practices, because of the lack of relevant skills and common awareness. This causes the low level of ICT penetration in the private and public sectors, decreasing acquisition of the benefits and efficiency gains associated with the Internet under the present economic conditions.

The role of the Internet is also limited by the insufficient development of market relations in various areas of the economy and the citizens' low paying capacity. Despite the fact that the internal process of a national market economy formation has already been under way for quite a long period of time, the results, in terms of providing stimuli for the ICT development, have been very modest. Nevertheless, the ICT market is formed and is in the process of a gradual liberalization.

At least two problems should be solved in order to increase the level of the ICT development of Ukraine – to expand a societal base of the ICT utilization and to increase the level of awareness of the population at large. In order to attain the above aims, ICT must be more widely applied in educational curricula and by innovative educational programmes that meet the demands of various social groups. These are also general preconditions for elimination of the digital divide both in cities and rural areas.

The primary tasks centred on furthering a sustainable ICT development includes in particular the following:

- Elaboration and application of new economic approaches in the ICT related areas;
- Establishment of a financial aid system for all players whose activities are connected with ICT practical application;
- Consolidation of the state and non-governmental structures that are active in the area related to ICT development and application;
- Promotion of computer literacy;
- Creation of proper preconditions for the formation and development of contemporary intellectual workforce market;
- Establishment of conditions for the provision of technical opportunities for national and international broadband Internet access;
- Education and training of highly-qualified personnel in the sphere of economic and information management, including marketing, advertisement, trade and finance, etc.;

- Creation of digital information resources, including e-libraries, e-exhibitions etc;
- Establishment of all-Ukrainian information computerized system, a "national scientific-educational environment", and promotion of Ukraine's integration into the system of world research and educational networks.

The realization of the "Electronic Ukraine" Programme will undoubtedly help the implementation of the above tasks if all the players demonstrate their willingness to take an active part in its implementation. Its implementation seems unimaginable without the proper support of the international community that already currently supports various ICT related projects in Ukraine.

Most of the above tasks concern education, which nowadays is unthinkable without a wide use of ICT means. The efforts undertaken and the results achieved in this area are highlighted below.

4. ICT for science and education

4.1. Present state of the education network

The Presidium of the National Academy of Sciences of Ukraine (NUAS) has carried out an analysis of the development and state of ICT in Ukraine and has come to the following conclusion: "It is at breaking point".

The Presidium and Institutes of NUAS have no corporate network and have been using telephone lines and the services of several providers. Existing lines have a data transfer rate of up to 56 kb/s. They do not guarantee quality of service and effectiveness of information retrieval. The rates are a great deal less than what is required for important scientific purposes.

Scientific investigation, virtual libraries, virtual laboratories, distance education are based on the principles of shells and include data interchange and data processing in the form of sound, visual, and graphic information. The existing network in this field cannot interact with other networks.

There has been a rapid development of ICT in the advanced countries. The annual growth of the world ICT market turnover is 10 per cent, and the Internet network has been extending at an unprecedented pace. The possibility of distance training and realization of international scientific projects, in which many researchers from dozens of countries can participate, has been realized thanks to the Internet enabling the development of highly effective technological and national academic computer networks.

It should be admitted that Ukraine is at the initial stage of telecommunication networks development. In this field, Ukraine should carry out a large volume of organizational, social and technical work to build up a desired level of capacity to effectively participate in these international networks.

The basic directions of the computer network development

The development of a computer network, according to the global prevalent trends, is one of the basic conditions for Ukraine to enter the advanced world community.

Three directions are considered:

- Development of connections with the global computer networks;
- Development of a national computer network ENTRONET. The networks of education, science, space research, networks of special assignment were considered as most forward looking and, thus, to be the first to be integrated with; and
- Development of corporate computer networks.

The build up of a national computer network and corporate networks was considered, taking into account the following factors:

- Ukrainian national and corporate networks have their own information environment in some spheres of activity, which are typical for Ukrainian economy branches, organizations, and groups;
- Since the national and corporate networks do not require servers and connecting channels to the global networks, the volume of internal information interchange is much greater, and the cost is less; and
- This makes easier to protect information with a downturn of the network level.

Development of a Ukrainian scientific and educational network

The development of a Ukrainian national scientific and educational network is a necessary stage of development of the scientific and educational sphere.

The network should ensure:

- Databases on knowledge in different areas of science, culture and education. Access to electronic libraries;
- Work of virtual scientific and educational laboratories;
- Work of virtual creative studios;
- Multi-service information processing
- Opportunity of distance education
- Significant intellectual accumulation
- Organization and support of scientific conferences

Creating the Ukrainian scientific and educational information network

The need for developing a Ukrainian information network for the science and education spheres became apparent at the beginning of the 1990s. However, the real opportunity to start this work only appeared in 1995, when the National Technical University "Kiev Polytechnic Institute" (NTUU "KPI") won a competition under the "Tempus-Tacis" programme on the creation of such a network in Ukraine with the participation of Aachen Technical University (Germany) and Delft University (Netherlands). The project was actively supported by the National Academy of Sciences of Ukraine and by the Ukrainian Ministry of Education and Science. From this time on, efforts towards the creation of the all-Ukrainian information network have been carried out. Below are presented some main stages of the implementation of the project:

- NUAS and the Ukrainian Ministry of Education and Science started the Programme on the creation of a National telecommunication science and education network in 1996. The network was named URAN (Ukrainian Research and Academic Network).

- In 1997, the Presidium of NUAS together with the Ukrainian Ministry of Education and Science founded the Association of URAN users, and the European Integration Centre was created to carry out the function of network operator.

- The task of creating the Ukrainian information science and education network with basic sites in the biggest educational and scientific centres (Kiev, Dnepropetrovsk, Donetsk, Kharkov, Odessa, and Lvov) was included in the 1997 National Informatization Programme.

- The URAN project was approved by the International Congress of UNESCO "Education and computer science" in October 1998.

- The first phase, covering major sites of Kiev, Kharkov, Dnepropetrovsk, Lvov, Odessa, and Donetsk, was completed in 1998-2000.

- The implementation of the second phase of URAN in Simferopol, Chernigov, Lugansk, Summy, Zaporozhie, and Ivano-Frankovsk began in 2001.

4.2. Network architecture

The construction of URAN is a necessary stage for the further development of the science and education spheres. It should have a significant intellectual content, contain databases and knowledge from different branches of science and education, electronic libraries, a system of information search, provide general remote usage with powerful computing resources, work in a mode of virtual scientific and educational laboratories, carry out multi-service processing of information (graphic, video and audio information).

The choice of URAN architecture is justified by its geographical, technical and information aspects. The URAN network was created on the model of the most powerful scientific and educational networks of Germany (DFN) and the Netherlands (SURFNET).

URAN has a three-level architecture. The first level includes the central node in Kiev and has the main optical fiber and satellite channels of data transfer, connected to the global Internet network. The second level includes the network regional nodes. The third level comprises its own information infrastructure and corporate networks of universities, academic institutions, scientific libraries that are corporate users of all URAN resources. The central site carries out general administration of the network and connects the users of the Kiev region. The base sites at other regional centres in Ukraine carry out similar functions at their level. The general network topology with allocation of the base and regional URAN centres is shown below.

The central URAN site in Kiev includes network operations centres, which are located at the Ukrainian Ministry of Education and Science, at the Cybernetic Centre of the National Academy of Sciences and at the National Technical University of Ukraine. The topology of the URAN network segment in Kiev includes academic institutions and universities.

URAN Topology in 2003

Internet exchange point
IX-UA –10 Mbps

Internet satellite channel
1,2Mbps

Chernigiv

Lutsk Rivne Zhitomyr Kyiv Sumy

Western RC
Lviv Kharkiv RC

Khmelnitskiy Poltava Lugansk

Ternopil Cherkasy

Ivano-Frankivsk Vinnutsa Dnipropetrovsk RC

Uzhgorod Kirovograd Donetsk RC

Chernivtsi Kriviy Rig Zaporizhzhe Mariupol

Mikolayiv

Kherson

Odesa RC Crimea RC
Simferopol

Sevastopol

★ Regional centres
★ Active regional nodes
— Digital TDM channels 64-128 kbps
— Digital TDM channels 256-2048 kbps
— Frame Relay 128/64 kbps
★— Analog channels 3000 bps
☆····☆ 2002-2003
★······· Perspective 2004

URAN structure map at 2003

The Kiev segment covers the Academgorodok area with a site at the Institute of Metallophysics of NUAS. The Western site is at the Institute of Electrodynamics of NUAS; the Southern site is at the Cybernetic Centre. Two central sites are at the Ukrainian Ministry of Education and Science and at the National Technical University of Ukraine.

The URAN topology is star-shaped with reserve segments, which are caused by application of asynchronous transfer mode (ATM) networking technology. This technology is a base for high-speed global networks. In addition, mail data link channels for the national telecommunication provider Ukrtelecom and the biggest corporate networks are constructed with this technology. This brings about unity of the technological platforms of the URAN network.

The URAN network is constructed with a uniform ideology that is based on the optimum selection of hardware-software platforms and balanced regional information resources distribution

Following international experience, URAN uses different types of communication channels – main ground channels of Ukrtelecom, own satellite channels and so-called "last mile communications" constructed with the use of microwave technologies for the connection of collective users, especially remote ones. The domestic microwave data link systems can be used in remote districts because of the absence of ground communication channels.

The URAN system can work in an optimum mode in terms of communication channels load, because the information about channels load is common and accessible to URAN users. The three-level structure of URAN is due to the character of information flows and services, as the information resources and networking servers are divided into central, regional and corporate ones.

4.3. Informational and intellectual content

Nowadays, URAN combines information on scientific and educational resources of more than 50 universities and scientific institutions located at their information servers in all Ukrainian regions. The task of URAN is the creation and provision of their own information resources and Internet resources to the network users. However, taking into account the necessity of remote education system development in Ukraine and its methodical maintenance, the resources of regional URAN sites are united with the network and resources of the regional remote training centres. In addition, the task of the regional centres is the integration of the resources of the electronic libraries for creation of the united national network of electronic libraries with powerful reference systems. The international project of electronic libraries, with the participation of the Academic Vernadsky's National Library, Scientific and Technical Library of NTUU "KPI", Vienna National Library (Austria), Aachen University (Germany) and Delft University (Netherlands), is now being implemented.

The provision of multi services to the scientific and educational networks is the main function of URAN. There are the following services:

- Data multicast – allows data transfer from one source to many consumers. Videoconference is a typical example of this kind of service;
- Network news;
- Buffering or temporary preservation (caching) of information resources – allows saving resources of communication channels, in particular of external channels;
- Connection to remote powerful computing resources;
- E-mail services;
- Functioning of the address book (directory) – allows people to search in the mode of "white pages" or organizations search in the mode of "yellow pages", etc.

Information protection in URAN

Taken separately, the resources of the URAN network certainly do not contain information that can be classified as a state secret. But the resources of the network users can contain various data, including information with limited access. Therefore, information generalized by all network or by a specific segment of the network is not desirable for non-authorized access. For these reasons, the organization of a scientific and educational network as national (establishment of direct communication channels between net points, application of appropriate specialized software and means) is a necessary condition to prevent possible non-authorized access.

Financial aspects of URAN network development

The majority of expenses associated with network development (re-equipment, user connection, operational expenses, etc.) are covered by such URAN users as universities and academic institutions (53 per cent), international grants (40 per cent) and state financing (7 per cent). However, the higher education and science system, and the information segment of this system cannot exist without essential State support. The activity of the URAN network is not profitable, all resources are directed to network development, and all financial activity is based on self-repayment principles. On the other hand, large-scale network development is possible only at the expense of the limited resources of scientific and educational establishments and by means of international projects. In addition, the majority of the international projects can be accepted for consideration only on condition of their parity financing by the parties. Therefore multi-channel financing is a necessary condition for the balanced development of components of scientific and educational information infrastructure, data links, administration system, and personnel training.

4.4. Use of network technologies in scientific research

While generalizing the numerous directions of the application of modern information technologies in Ukraine, it is possible to classify them into the following: State management and economy; environment, medicine, biology; scientific research and critical technologies; education; culture; mass media; Internet technologies.

Among the scientific spheres, where the network technologies are applied directly, the following can be chosen: information technologies in environment, medicine and biology. They are connected with:

- Methods of analysis of the environment;
- Methods of analysis and forecasting of accidents;
- Technologies of risk estimation for environmentally dangerous manufacturing; forecasting and decision-making in emergency situations;
- Systems of equipment design; and
- Systems of diagnostic and decision-making in medicine and biology including application of telemedical technologies.

These problems were particularly urgent after the accident at the Chernobyl Nuclear Power Plant.

A project to create agent-guided technologies for search, preservation, processing and transfer of information units, network technologies in scientific research is directed to intellectualization of the networks similar to URAN. The Cybernetic Centre of the National Academy of Sciences has implemented this project. Agency platforms are indispensable for the scientific and educational network environment.

Virtual research laboratories are an important direction of network technologies application in science. They allow scientists from different parts of the world to be involved in carrying out research inside the laboratories with further information interchange through a computer network. Joint work of the Glushkov Institute of Cybernetics and Florida

University (USA) on the project of discrete optimization for information coding is an example of such a virtual laboratory activity using URAN.

One more direction of the application of network technologies is electronic commerce, including the market of technologies, know-how, and scientific production. This kind of activity is particularly important for Ukrainian science, industry and technologies and should occupy an appropriate place in the structure of the market. Electronic commerce and transfer of high technologies will permit Ukraine to come into the world community.

4.5. Use of network technologies for educational purposes

The application of computer networks in education is linked to the development of the newest educational and training programmes, the use of Internet technologies in the educational process, the creation of electronic libraries, reference systems, systems of management in education, automation and information support for the circulation of documents ("Osvita" system), use of specialized databanks and knowledge, and distance education.

One of the most typical educational technologies is distance education:

- Distance education is not an alternative but additional;
- Distance education has no geographical or political borders;
- It is a form of mass training and individual training at the same time, i.e. each user obtains knowledge that is necessary only for him, at the appropriate speed;
- This form of training is based on motivation, i.e. it is effective for people interested in obtaining knowledge as "goods" in order to use it in a career.

From the point of view of economic development and global division of labour this training technology has the following attractive features:

- It is highly dynamic as regards the needs of the rapidly changing labour market demand;
- It greatly surpasses the traditional system of education as regards the opportunity to obtain the necessary volume of knowledge from world databases and bases of knowledge; and
- The speed of knowledge updating is unsurpassed.

At the national level, the system of distance education comprises: coordinating and serving organizations, distance education and professional orientation centres, educational and scientific institutions, developers and students of the system, using URAN resources, uniform catalogues, databanks and knowledge, and information resources.

The system methodology of distance education is based upon the principles of shells, comprising the internal structure of the system and its connections. In the shell only the information content and organizational information can change. Other general-system modules of the shell remain unchanged.

Structure of distance learning system at the national level

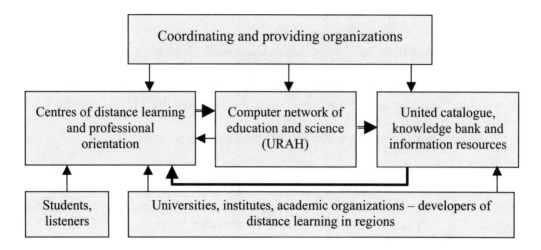

Distance Education Constituency

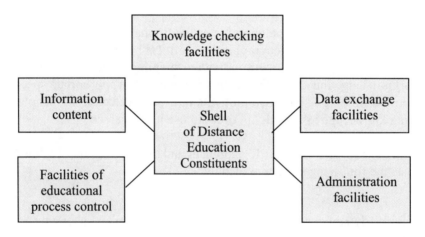

The interactive dialogue between student and teacher is carried out in two modes:

- Synchronous (on-line) mode in the form of discussions, seminars, conferences; and
- Asynchronous (off-line) mode in the form of electronic correspondence (e-mail) or forums.

Thus, the student can be at home, at the workplace or in a computer class, receiving lectures, educational material, passing tests, communicating with the teachers through a telecommunication network. The only fixed elements are laboratory sessions (for some educational programmes); examination sessions (examinations, tests) and projects, where students defend their degree.

The Ukrainian Centre of distance education has been established in order to coordinate work for the creation of a distance education system in Ukraine and the step-by-step introduction of its elements into the system of the Ukrainian Ministry of Education and

Science on the basis of NTUU "KPI". The centre creates the documents that concern distance education; adapts the most effective educational information software; develops distance classes; prepares the teachers, methodologists, managers, programmers, and system managers for this form of education; creates, approves and distributes distance technologies of education.

It should be noted that the creation of a distance class is difficult and challenging work, far from trivial from the methodical point of view. On the global market, the price of one class is between US$ 15,000 and US$ 30,000. The centre has involved experts from educational institutions of Ukraine and has created 50 classes from different disciplines.

The introduction of distance education provides for the appropriate technological equipment that is connected with the requirements of telecommunication networks of information interchange with a data rate of 1 Mb/s and more. The URAN network can fulfil this function fully.

4.6. Prospects of the evolution of information network systems in science and education

The main problem is the absence of a complex state programme aimed at promoting the evolution of the scientific and educational network. There is therefore no steady financial and organizational support from the State. This is why the URAN network does not cover all Ukrainian regions.

Ukraine needs a highly effective scientific and educational network to capitalize its intellectual assets. It should replicate one of the most well known world scientific and educational networks: DFN, B-WIN (Germany), SUPER JANET (Great Britain), SURFNET (Netherlands), RENATER-2 (France), CANET-2 (Canada) to be able to compete at the global market of intellectual products. There are other scientific and educational national and regional networks, such as the Russian ones (RBNET, RUNET, RELARN, RSSI, MSUNET, FREENET, PAH/ORC), which could be used as a prototype.

The next problem is the absence of essential steps at the State level towards linking the Ukrainian scientific and educational information segment to the European and the world information space. At the same time, the global tendency is the integration of national scientific and educational networks. The European transnational network TEN-155, with a bit rate of 155 Mb/s, has therefore been converted to the scientific and educational network GEANT that already uses fibre optic data-transmission channels with a rate of up to 1 Tb/s. The information scientific network SINSEE of Southern and East European countries is also rapidly developing.

The important perspectives of the evolution of the URAN system in the near future (with appropriate investments) are the following:

- evolution of a backbone in all regions of Ukraine, escalating of nodes and trunk data-transmission channels power;
- creation of URAN information resources and evolution of regional network segments and regional nodes; and

- creation of its own satellite external and terrestrial data-transmission channels, the decision of "last mile" problem by connection of end users using microwave information technologies.

Once these plans are implemented, a data rate up to 4 Mbps in 2002 and more than 10 Mbps would be possible.

The important problem is the integration of the URAN network, already accepted by international organizations as the national scientific and educational network of Ukraine, into the trans-European scientific data networks GEANT and SINSEE.

The next step is the creation of the Ukrainian Internet segment and the development of trunk fibre optic data-transmission channels. In this segment, the URAN network is one of the most important elements. Total transmission capacity of external channels of the Ukrainian Internet segment is increasing; the data rate, which was 80 Mb/s in mid-2000, is now more than 100 Mb/s.

The National Academy of Sciences, the Ukrainian Ministry of Education and Science, the State Committee of Ukraine on Communication, Ukrtelecom and other government institutions and departments can jointly solve the problem of data rate increase.

Thus, under limited State resources, the introduction of the National telecommunication network of science and education will allow the evolution of these strategic important spheres to be speeded up and will simplify Ukraine's joining the world scientific and educational community.

Conclusion

It should be acknowledged that the deep economic crisis that occurred in Ukraine since its independence at the beginning of the 1990es now seems to be over. The economic growth registered during the last few years allows us to expect that Ukraine will be in a position to allocate more resources to the innovation sphere thus promoting the development of information and communication technologies indispensable for entering the knowledge-based economy club.

At present, there are signs that the process of transition to a market economy has been accelerating, and the well being of the population is on the road to improvement. The availability of highly educated and talented people in the country makes it possible to suggest that with a steady growth of the national economy, the perspectives of a rapid ICT development in the country are highly plausible. Ukraine even now is among the most developed countries as compared with other newly independent states. Still much remains to be done in developing a proper legislative basis and transformation of sometimes outdated institutional and industrial infrastructure which are needed for future knowledge-based economy.

Annex I. Knowledge-Based Economy Indicators

1. Network Access

1.1. Information infrastructure

• Telephone penetration (number of mainlines per 100 people)

20-23 per 100 people at the beginning of 2002. It varies widely from 45.4% in Kiev to just several percent in rural areas.

• Mobile wireless penetration (%), growth trend

Less than 4.5% at the beginning of 2002, growth in 1999-2000 was 180-190%

Growth of mobile phone users by years

	Number of users (thousands)	Growth (%)
1998	100	100
1999	280	180
2000	814	190
2001	2,223	173

• Total number of mobile telephone subscribers

2320 thousands at the beginning of 2002

Number of mobile phone users by operators for the beginning of 2002

Operator	Number of users (thousands)
Kyiv star	1100
UMC	1045
Golden Telecom	70
DCC	42
Wellcom	33.5
Astelit	30

• Total number of mobile telephone subscribers per 1000 people

47 per 1000 people in 2001

• Wireless penetration (percentage of the population), growth trend

Less than 1%

• Total number of cable TV subscribers

2.640 thousands in 2000

• Cable TV subscribers, % of households

N/A

1.2. Internet availability

• Total number of ISP providers

238 in Ukraine as a whole and 79 in Kiev

• Prevailing types of ISPs' networks (microwaves/radio…)

Dial-up lines: 626 in Ukraine as a whole and 113 in Kiev

• % of unsuccessful local calls

N/A

• Is there competition among ISP providers?

Yes, the market is competitive. Its consolidation is expected in the coming years.

• What are opportunities for public Internet access (libraries, Internet-cafes, etc.)?

More than 3,000 Internet-cafés and computer clubs are working in Ukraine. Only 30 % of all computer clubs have total Internet access in Ukraine, and up to 50% have Internet access in the cities. 70% of Internet connections are by dial-up, 20% by dedicated lines, and 10% by cable TV. Distribution of Internet clubs in large cities of Ukraine is as follows: Kiev – 400, Dnepropetrovsk – 300, Kharkov – 280, Odessa –230, Donetsk – 200 and Lvov- 200. 2.8% of pupils have total Internet access in Ukraine. 3.5% of pupils have Internet access in the cities, and 1.3% of pupils have Internet access in rural schools. The national electronic network of Ukrainian libraries was created on the basis of three libraries -Parliament Library, V. Vernadsky National Library, and the library of T. Shevchenko National University. This network has more than 40 partners. 24 regional libraries have Internet access. The Ukrainian library is a project of the Euro-Atlantic Foundation and has high-quality and useful information about Ukraine and the world.

• Are there dedicated line lease possibilities? Are there competing providers?

There are no limitations. The possibility of leasing is defined by paying capacity.

1.3. Internet affordability

- What are the prices of Internet access (unlimited access, per minute charge)?

Dial-up in 2002 (US dollars)

Company	Data rate, kbps	Unlimited dial-up
Farlep	56	30
Infocom	56	30
IP Telecom	56	15
Lucky Net	56	25
Optima Telecom	56	29
Relcom	56	40

Dedicated lines in 2002 (US$)

Company	Data rate, Mbps	Dedicated line 64k per month	Dedicated line 128k per month
Farlep	64	400	800
Infocom	2	250	440
Lucky Net	56	100	350
Optima Telecom	64	120	230
Relcom	33.6	350	650

- Is it affordable for majority/minority (compare with average salary/income)?

It is not affordable for the majority of population 31% of which lives on less than US$ 2 per day and 80% of which described themselves as poor.

- What are the rates for leasing lines?

N/A

- Are the rates affordable for small businesses or individuals?

Internet is expensive for small business and for most individual users.

1.4. Network speed and quality

- What is the percentage of successful calls?

N/A

- What is the quality of voice connection?

N/A

31

• How many faults are reported per year for each 100 telephone mainlines?

N/A

• How long does it take to clear faults (48 hours, a week, month)?

N/A

• Which services are supported by local telecommunications infrastructure: e-mail, high-speed modem connection, what is the maximum speed?

All kinds of services are supported by the existing network.

• Are there sufficient backbone facilities/networks? Even for peak demand?

N/A

• What is the percentage of packet loss by the network?

N/A

1.5. Hardware and software

• Are there local IT hardware/software sales points?

More than 500 companies are engaged in the computer market. 1.3 million computers were sold in 2001. Computer stores are in all cities of Ukraine. The internal market of software is estimated at US$ 40 million.

• Is the price of IT hardware/software affordable for majority/minority of citizens/businesses?

Computer prices are moderate for the minority of the people and for most enterprises.

Estimated prices for computers without monitor (US$)

Name	Average minimum price	Average maximum price
PC	300	600
Notebook	1,000	1,500
PIII server	2,000	4,000
PIII Xeon server	5,000	10,000
PIV server	7,000	15,000

• Is there software in local languages?

N/A

32

• Is software imported or adapted locally? (percentage of the imported, adapted, produced locally hardware or software in total number in circulation)

Both

• Is there a broad variety/some/very few software business applications?

N/A

• Are the IT software/hardware retail and wholesale markets competitive and vibrant?

N/A

1.6. Service and support

• How long is the waiting period for telephone line instalment? (total number of those on the waiting list; waiting period: days, weeks, months, years)

Non-satisfied demand for telephones

Year	Number in thousands
1992	3,685
1995	3,410
1998	2,737
1999	2,655
2000	2,483

• How long is the waiting period for reported telephone line problem to be fixed? (minutes, hours, days and etc.)

N/A

• Are there software developers, web designers, network administrators and other technical personnel, and how many (working where, employed/ unemployed)?

Nearly 50,000 people are engaged in the field of software. Nearly 15,000 people are graduates in the field of ICT. Salaries in the field of ICT are between US$ 200 and US$ 2,000 per month.

Unemployment in the field of ICT

	1999	2000
Number of registered unemployed people	1,205,000	1,188,000
ICT	1,900	1,700

33

2. Networked Learning

2.1. Schools' access to ICTs

• Are there computers in schools? How many students per computer? At which level (university/secondary/primary)?

8,244 schools out of 21,226 (38.2%) have computers. In rural schools this radio is 26%. 21% of computers in the schools have modern processors.

Schools' access to computers

	Cities	Rural schools	Total
Schools	6,506	14,720	21,226
Schools with computers	4,239	3,801	8,040
Computer classes	4,009	3,494	7,503
Total number of computers	55,852	35,155	91,007

• Who has access to computers (technical staff/faculty/students)?

Computer access for pupils

Computer access	Cities, %	Villages, %
Schools	27.2	12.1
Home	16	3.3
Clubs	29.6	11.7
Internet access in schools	3.5	1.3

Computer access for teachers

Computer access	
Schools	12 %
Home	13.3%
Clubs	14.1%
Internet access in schools	22%

• What is the quality of hardware (386/486/Pentium…)?

N/A

• Are there LANs in schools? Regional WANs? National school networks?

N/A

• Do schools have Internet connectivity? Is it dial up or through a leased line, wireless?

N/A

2.2. Enhancing education with ICTs

• What are the computers used for? What is the level of computer literacy/skills?

There are 3,729 educational institutions that have software for education, of which 2,341 are situated in cities, and 388 in villages. One half of 21,100 programme packages concern computer science. The Centre of Secondary Education organizes a contest of computer programmes. Thirteen universities work jointly in the field of computer education.

• What is the level of information and communication technologies integration in the curriculum?

Curricula on programming exist in all universities of Ukraine. All private and state educational institutions propose education in the field of computer science.

2.3. Developing the ICT workforce

• Are there training opportunities for programming, maintenance, and support?

As stated above, curricula on programming exist in all universities of Ukraine.

• Who is offering them (public/private centres)?

As stated above, all private and state educational institutions propose education in the field of computer science.

• Are they affordable for majority/minority of the population?

They are affordable for the minority of population

• Is on-line training available?

Shevchenko National University, UNESCO, and CISCO SYSTEMS founded the Network Academy in Ukraine which has been working October 2001. Since then 200 specialists have graduated.

• Do employers offer training?

Yes. Employers propose education in the field of computer science for their employees also. Education of accountants and economists is the most widespread.

3. Networked Society

3.1. People and organization online

• What is the percentage of the population which: Is aware of Internet existence? Has used Internet recently? Uses Internet regularly?

Share of population in %

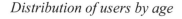

• What is the structure of users by gender, age, social and educational status?

Distribution of users by age

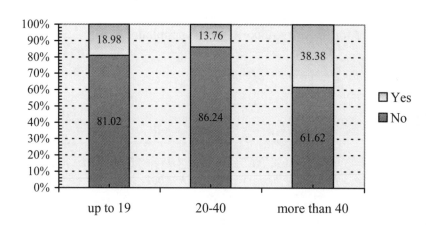

Distribution of users by profession

Students	93.7 %
Businessmen	93 %
Employees	85.8%
Pensioners	44%
Farmers	26.8%

• What is the number locally registered domain names (per 1000 people)?

36

N/A

• Is there advertising for online companies, and how common is it?

N/A

3.2. Locally relevant content

• Are there (and how many: no, few, some, many) websites:

There are more than 15,000 Ukrainian websites.

• How often are they updated and is content static or dynamic?

Renewal of the content is slow and static.

• Are the above web sites created in the community?

N/A

• Are bulletin board systems, Usenet groups, newsletters, and/or listservs in use?

Bulletin board systems, Usenet groups, newsletters, and listservs are used.

• Are there opportunities for Web-related training?

There are opportunities for Web-related training.

3.3. ICTs in Everyday life

• Does population include information and communication technologies (phones, faxes, pagers, computers) in everyday life?

People use ICT (phone, faxes, pagers, computers) in everyday life. Especially widespread use of ICT is in Kiev and other major cities.

• Are there phones, wireless phones, digital assistants, pagers, PCs and are they being used regularly? Are they used for household commerce (banking, online shopping, investing) and social and commercial interaction (bartering, online chat and etc.)

Private users own 275,00–327,000 computers used for e-mail, Internet, job and games. ICT is almost not used for household commerce (banking, online shopping, investing).

• Are there PCs with e-mail capability available (cyber cafés, telecenters) and are they being widely used?

There are nearly 3,000 computer clubs and Internet cafes

3.4. ICTs in the workplace

• Do employees have:

- (Un)limited access to phones?

Access to phones for work purposes is mostly unlimited

- Personal e-mail accounts?

Nearly every employee has an e-mail account if he or she has a computer and Internet access.

- Internet access from personal workstations?

Nearly every employee has an Internet access if he or she has a computer.

- E-mail and web addresses on business cards?

Web addresses and e-mail are noted on business cards.

• What percentage of businesses and government offices have computers, how many of them, how many employees use them?

The number of computers is 150,000, and 30% of them are not modem. The level of computer supply is nearly 54%.

• Are they networked?

N/A

• Is business mostly conducted in person or by e-mail, or are there data sharing, enterprise, reporting, transaction, and research applications? How intensively are they used?

Business is mostly managed personally.

• Are there efficiency gains resulting from the use of ICT systems?

N/A

4. Networked Economy

4.1. ICT employment opportunities

• Are there opportunities for technically skilled workers within the country?

More than 800 companies are engaged in ICT. From 5,000 to 7,000 groups of 2-80 persons work in ICT temporarily.

• Are companies from outside of the country investing in IT related projects?

There are foreign investments in the field of ICT.

• What is the proportion of knowledge workers and information related business in the economy? (percentage of labour force, percentage of GDP)?

N/A

• Are businesses considering IT in their strategies?

Use of ICT is becoming part of general companies' strategy.

4.2. B2C electronic commerce

B2C Electronic commerce is at the initial stage of development. There are many electronic shops but there are no significant profits from their activity. Internet is used mostly as an information and search machine.

• Do local businesses have websites and how many? Is content current or static?

N/A

• Are there online B2C transactions, or are transactions mainly oral and/or paper-based, phone or fax-based?

N/A

• Is online retail noticeable component of the overall commercial activity?

N/A

4.3. B2B electronic commerce

B2B Electronic commerce is almost absent

• What are the sources of market information, are they sufficient for providing transparency?

N/A

• Are there online B2B transactions, or are transactions mainly oral, paper-based, phone or fax-based?

N/A

• Can transactions be conducted online without any paper documents? Is the process automated? Does it allow online tracking, monitoring?

N/A

• What portion of B2B activity is conducted on-line? Is there gain in efficiency?

N/A

4.4. E-Government

• Number of government resources online? Does it include information, hours of operation, any services? Is information current and relevant?

All Ukrainian authorities have websites including: President of Ukraine, Ukrainian Parliament, Council of National Security and Defense of Ukraine, Cabinet of Ministers, all Ministries of Ukraine, all State Committees, all Supreme Court authorities, National Bank of Ukraine, State Tax Administration of Ukraine and others. There is a Government Portal from which all these entities can be accessed. Information is in many instances available in English in addition to Ukrainian and Russian.

• Is there online interaction between government and citizens, government and suppliers and contractors, or is interaction mainly oral, paper-based, phone or fax-based?

Interaction between government and citizens, suppliers and contractors is mainly oral, paper-based, phone and fax-based.

• Is there online interaction between government and suppliers and contractors, or is the interaction mainly oral, paper-based, phone or fax-based?

N/A

- Is it possible to download applications from the web sites?

N/A

- Can citizens apply for permits, licenses, and taxes on line?

N/A

5. Network Policy

5.1. Telecommunications regulation

- Is liberalization of telecommunications sector planned or implemented?

Yes, it is expected to be liberalised further

- Is there competition between telecommunications service providers?

Ukrtelecom has a monopoly in telecommunications and controls all local lines and national infrastructure.

- Is broadband Internet access offered?

Yes, but on a limited scale. There are plans to expand broadband access.

- Is regulation set and enforced by an independent body?

The State Committee of Communications and Informatization is the regulating authority. The Committee has the following functions: licensing, tariffs, distribution of phone numbers, policy, stocks management, budget projects, distribution of radio frequency spectrum.

5.2. ICT trade policy

- Do tariffs or other restrictions (technical standards, domestic regulation, etc.) exist?

There are restrictions for offering fixed communication services. Ukrtelecom has exclusive rights for offering these services.

Tariffs (US$)

Number of lines	Installation and connection	Payment per month	Deposit for international calls
1-2	1,000	50	200
3-9	800	40	150
10-19	600	30	100
20 and more	250	20	100

Services (US$)

Services	For people	For commercial companies
Installation and connection	40	160
Local calls	0.0039 per minute	0.0062 per minute
Intercity calls	0.0192-0.06 per minute	0.03-0.06 per minute
International calls	0.257-2.448 per minute	0.257-2.448 per minute

• Are there restrictions in the service (including information services) sector?

N/A

• Are there disproportional taxes on electronically delivered services?

N/A

• Is Foreign Direct Investment in IT sector existent, and is it encouraged, discouraged, restricted?

N/A

6. Media

6.1. Radio, TV and newspapers

• Number of Radio and TV stations, newspapers, the size of audience/circulation

Number of radios per 1000 people – 860 (1995) and 889 (2000). Number of TV sets per 1000 people – 372 (1995) and 456 (2000). Daily newspapers per 1000 people – 45 (1995) and 101 (2000).

6.2. Employment in the media

• Number of employees in the media

N/A

• Trend: is the number increasing/decreasing?

N/A

7. Intellectual Capital

7.1. Patents

• How many are issued per annum?

Number of patents granted to residents of Ukraine and non-residents

Year	Residents	Non-residents	Total
2001	6,763	114	6877
2000	4,921	851	5,772
1999	619	675	1,294
1998	4,225	111	4,336
1997	8,709	412	9,121
1996	4,085	185	4270

• What are the trends?

See above

7.2. Copyrights

• How many are issued per annum?

N/A

• What are the trends?

N/A

7.3. Licenses

• How many are issued per annum?

N/A

• What are the trends?

N/A

7.4. Trademarks

• How many are issued per annum?

Number of marks registered in the name of residents of Ukraine and non-residents

Year	Residents	Non-residents	Total
2000	1,372	6,701	6,073
1999	1,742	6,136	7,678
1998	935	6,321	7,256
1997	788	5,932	6,720
1996	493	5,117	5,610

• What are the trends?

See above

7.5. Scientific and/or technical associations

• List with a brief profile

N/A

8. Education

8.1. Higher education

• Total number of higher education establishments (public/private).

Total amount of higher educational institutions (state and private)

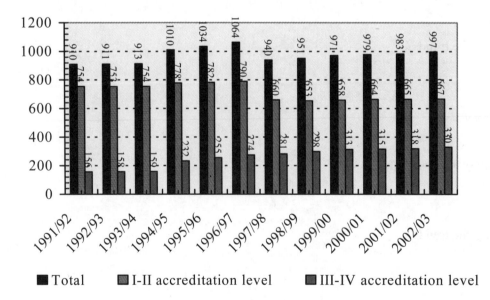

• Total number of students (total average per annum, in the private and in the public sector)

Number of students per 10,000 citizens

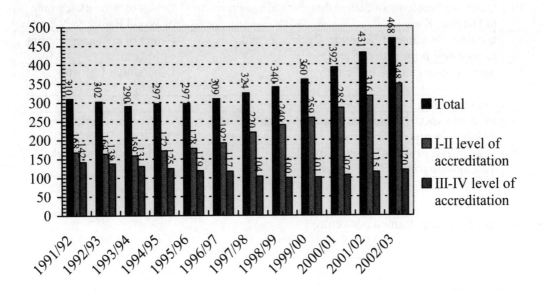

• Prevailing specializations (distribution of students among the fields)

N/A

• Cumulative number of population with higher education degrees (total and in science and technology fields)

N/A

8.2. Distant learning

• Distant learning facilities

State of network learning for June 2002

№	Educational institution	Subdivision of network learning
1	Shevchenko National University	ICC UNINET network
2	Ukrainian Center of Network Education, Kiev	URAN network
3	International Finance Institute, Kiev	Laboratory
4	National Technical University "Kharkov Polytechnical Institute", Kharkov	Laboratory of network learning
5	V. Glushkov Cybernetic Center, Kiev	UNESCO Center
6	Lvov Institute of Management, Lvov	UDL System
7	Nikopol Institute of Management, Business and Law,	Department

	Nikopol	
8	Kiev Institute of Investment Management, Kiev	Server
9	Kharkov Technical University of Radioelectronics, Kharkov	Laboratory of virtual network learning
10	Ukrainian Academy of State Administration at President of Ukraine, Kiev	Center of network learning of World Bank
11	Ukrainian Institute of Scientific, Technical, and Economical Information, Kiev	Center of computer learning SEMicom
12	Summy State University, Summy	Laboratory of network learning
13	Ternopol State Technical University, Ternopol	-
14	M. Zhukovsky National Aerospace University "Kharkov Aviation Institute", Kharkov	Center of network learning "Osvita"
15	State University of Informational and Telecommunication Technologies	Subdivision of network learning

• Number of students trained per centre

N/A

9. Labour Force

9.1. Employment in science and technical fields

Number of employees and trends in the fields

	1998	1999	2000	2001
Number of institutions that carry out scientific and technical works	1 518	1 506	1 490	1 479
Number of persons who carry out scientific and technical works	134 413	126 045	120 773	113 341
Volume of scientific and technical works carried out by actual prices (million Hryvnas)	1 269.0	1 578.2	1 978.4	2 275.0
Number of persons with drsc degree in Ukrainian economy	10 446*	10 233*	10 339*	10 603*
of persons with PhD degree in Ukrainian economy	59 703*	59 547*	58 741*	60 647*

* data for 1 October

• Compensation rates in the fields (average salaries)

N/A

9.2. Employment in electronics industry

• Number of employees and trends in the fields

46

N/A

• Compensation rates and trends in the fields
N/A

9.3. Employment in telecom industry

• Number of employees and trends in the fields

N/A

• Compensation rates and trends in the fields

N/A

10. Research and Development

10.1. Research institutions

• Number of research institutions

Number of R&D organisations by years

	1990	1995	1996	1997	1998	1999	2000	2001
Total	1,400	1,453	1,435	1,450	1,518	1,506	1,490	1,479

10.2. Investments in research and development

• The total amount, government and private business breakdown of total investment in research and development

Expenditures for R&D and distribution by type in million Hryvnas (current prices)

Year	Total	By type of performed R&D in %			
		Fundamental	Applied	Development	Services
1999	1264,9	16,2	21,4	54,6	7,8
2000	1636,3	15,8	22,9	52,2	9,1
2001	2010,7	16,7	14,4	54,8	14,1

Distribution of gross domestic expenditure on R&D by source of funds in %

Year	Business enterprise	Government	Higher education	Private non-profit	Funds from abroad
2000	31,4	39,3	0,1	-	29,2

Annex II

Bibliography

1. Common Country Assessment, the United Nations Country Team in Ukraine, UNDP, 2001
2. Ukraine and the Knowledge-based Economy: developing a national strategy, Ministry of Economy and European Integration of Ukraine, 2002
3. Contemporary issues of innovation policy in transition economy: lessons from Ukraine, Knowledge Economy Forum II co-sponsored by the World Bank and Finland, 2003
4. World Development Report 2003, World Bank, 2003
5. Human Development Report, UNDP, 2002
6. E-Policy Development in Transition Economis 2002-2003, UNECE, 2003
7. Statistical Yearbook of Ukraine for 2001, Ukraine, 2002
8. UNESCO Institute for Statistics, http://www.unesco.org/
9. WIPO Statistics, http://www.wipo.org/ipstats/en/